The Irresistible Garfield

BY: JIM DAVIS

GUILD PUBLISHING LONDON

This edition published 1986 by
Book Club Associates
by arrangement with
Ravette Limited

Reprinted 1987

Printed and bound in Great Britain
for Ravette Limited,
3 Glenside Estate, Star Road, Partridge Green,
Horsham, Sussex RH13 8RA
by William Clowes Limited, Beccles and London.

The Irresistible

How can you resist this lovable, adorable, cute example of 'felinity'. The wide-eyed smile, the cute button nose, those delicate features, and of course the warm hearted personality? Then of course there's Garfield..!

10-16

FOLD FOLD

JIM DAVIS   12-2

CAN I PLAY TOO?

SURE... GRAB HOLD

© 1981 United Feature Syndicate, Inc.

SLEEP ON MY TEDDY BEAR, WILL YOU?!

Z

JIM DAVIS   12-3

Z

I WISH I COULD DO THAT

Z

© 1981 United Feature Syndicate, Inc.

6-5   JIM DAVIS

MINE!

POOKY IS A ONE-CAT TEDDY BEAR

© 1981 United Feature Syndicate, Inc.

MUST YOU RUSH?

I GUESS I'LL BE LEAVING

JIM DAVIS

IF YOU INSIST, I'LL STAY

© 1981 United Feature Syndicate, Inc.

6-6

CHRISTMAS SPIRIT...

12-25   JIM DAVIS

IT'S NOT THE GIVING. IT'S NOT THE RECEIVING

IT'S THE LOVING. MERRY CHRISTMAS

© 1981 United Feature Syndicate, Inc.

WHAT A NICE CHRISTMAS. I GOT AN EYE FOR MY TEDDY BEAR, SAND FOR MY SANDBOX, AND A NEW BLANKET

12-26   JIM DAVIS

THIS IS WHAT HAPPINESS IS ALL ABOUT...

SECURITY

© 1981 United Feature Syndicate, Inc.

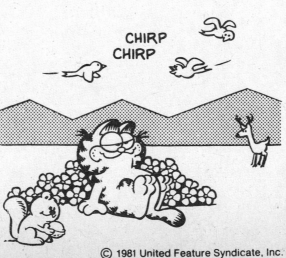

TONIGHT I AM GOING TO TAKE LIZ OUT **SOLO**. YOU ARE STAYING HOME, GARFIELD

JIM DAVIS   12-17

WHERE'S MY FAVORITE TIE?

© 1981 United Feature Syndicate, Inc.

I GET TO GO WITH YOU, AND THE TIE LIVES

WHAT SAY WE DOUBLE DATE, OLD BUDDY?

GOOD EVENING, LIZ. I HAVE A WONDERFUL TIME PLANNED FOR US

JIM DAVIS 12-18

WE'LL HAVE DINNER, GO TO A MOVIE, AND MANY MORE THINGS TOO NUMEROUS TO MENTION

© 1981 United Feature Syndicate, Inc.

YOU BROUGHT THE CAT

THAT WAS ONE OF THE UNMENTIONABLES

GOOD MORNING, GARFIELD. IS THERE SOMETHING YOU'RE TRYING TO TELL ME?

JIM DAVIS

IT'S THE CHRISTMAS SEASON, YOU SAY

12-20

GIMME, GIMME, GIMME, GIMME, GIMME, GIMME, GIMME, GIMME

JIM DAVIS   12-21

GIMME! GIMME! GIMME! GIMME! GIMME! GIMME!

I'M GETTING INTO THE CHRISTMAS SPIRIT

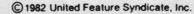

© 1982 United Feature Syndicate, Inc.

JON WILL BE CHECKING THIS TRAP SOON

© 1982 United Feature Syndicate, Inc.

MY BUNNY SLIPPERS?

THEY LIKE TO ROAM AT NIGHT

12-4

JIM DAVIS

JIM DAVIS

SPUT SPUT WEE EZE GURGLE SPUT

10-26

© 1982 United Feature Syndicate, Inc.

THE CAR HAS STOPPED AND IT'S GETTING DARK. WHAT SHOULD I DO, GARFIELD?

I CAN ONLY THINK OF ONE THING

MAKE IT GO!

GARFIELD, SOMETIMES I THINK YOU DON'T LIKE IT WHEN I HAVE DATES

ABSOLUTELY

JIM DAVIS

1-21

DATING LEADS TO MARRIAGE. MARRIAGE LEADS TO CHILDREN

AND DO YOU KNOW WHAT CHILDREN DO TO CATS?

© 1983 United Feature Syndicate, Inc.

I WONDER WHAT AWFUL THING IS GOING TO HAPPEN TO ME TODAY? MAYBE THE SKY WILL FALL. MAYBE ODIE WILL BRING HIS LONG LOST TWIN BROTHER HOME...

JIM DAVIS

2-7

OR WORSE YET, MAYBE NERMAL WILL COME FOR A VISIT

© 1983 United Feature Syndicate, Inc.

Garfield

The All-Round
Sports Star

BY: JIM DAVIS

The All-Round Sports Star

In the next 80 pages you will see a healthy Garfield; running, jumping, throwing, catching, jogging and exercising!

Running wild with his imagination, jumping to conclusions, throwing down his food, catching 'forty winks',

jogging his memory and exercising his wit.
This according to Garfield, is essential for a healthy appetite!

PTOOEY!

OKAY, GARFIELD.
NOW GIVE ME SOME
HIGH LOBS

PTOOEY!

PTOOEY!

6-3

JIM DAVIS

PTOOEY!

OKAY, GARFIELD. NOW GIVE ME SOME HIGH LOBS

© 1979 United Feature Syndicate, Inc.

8-5

JIM DAVIS

WHAT SAY I SWITCH OVER TO THE MOVIE, GANG?

NAH GRRR FFFT

SPLOOSH!

OH-NO! A VICIOUS UNDERTOW IS DRAGGING ME OUT TO SEA!

I'M TOO YOUNG TO GO!

9-9

I CAN SEE THE HEADLINES NOW... "WORLD FAMOUS CAT LOST AT SEA. MILLIONS OF BEAUTIFUL GIRL CATS GRIEF-STRICKEN!"

I CAN'T MAKE IT! I'M GOING DOWN FOR THE THIRD TIME!

© 1979 United Feature Syndicate, Inc.

I'D SAVE YOU, GARFIELD. BUT I'M NOT ABOUT TO GIVE A CAT MOUTH-TO-MOUTH RESUSCITATION

JiM DAViS

10-28

© 1979 United Feature Syndicate, Inc.

MUNCH
SMACK
SLURP

PTOOEY!

BURP

GARFIELD WENT TO SO
MUCH TROUBLE I HATED
TO SPOIL IT FOR HIM

JIM DAVIS

HAVE YOU EVER NOTICED HOW MUCH SOME PEOPLE LOOK LIKE THEIR PETS, GARFIELD?

© 1979 United Feature Syndicate, Inc.

HEE HEE

HEE

HA-HA HA

HA

12-2

JIM DAVIS

WOULD YOU LIKE TO COME IN, GARFIELD?

JIM DAVIS

12-9

1-27

© 1980 United Feature Syndicate, Inc.

JIM DAVIS

SAY, "AH," GARFIELD

2-1

I'LL TAKE YOUR TEMPERATURE IF YOU DON'T SAY, "AH"

AH

JIM DAVIS © 1980 United Feature Syndicate, Inc.

I KNOW YOU'RE JUST A VETERINARIAN, LIZ, BUT I'VE HAD THESE DIZZY SPELLS LATELY...

2-2

WELL NOW, WHY DON'T WE JUST CHECK YOUR BLOOD PRESSURE

UH... DOCTOR

JIM DAVIS © 1980 United Feature Syndicate, Inc.

2-17   JIM DAVIS

© 1980 United Feature Syndicate, Inc.

IT'S NOT THE HAVING,
IT'S THE GETTING

2·24

JiM DAViS

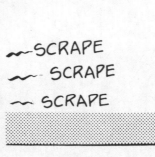

STAND ASIDE, LITTLE LADY. I'LL STOP THE TRAFFIC FOR YOU

JIM DAVIS

© 1980 United Feature Syndicate, Inc.

HOLD UP!

VOOM!

MY HERO

4-27

FACE IT, GARFIELD...

YOU AREN'T THE KITTEN YOU ONCE WERE

4-28

I'M MAKING SOME REALLY GREAT SOUP FOR SUPPER, GARFIELD

SOMETHING'S WRONG HERE

4-29

AND NOW SOME SEASONING...

I DON'T LIKE THE SOUND OF THIS

BATH TIME!

I'VE BEEN DUPED AGAIN!

JIM DAVIS

© 1980 United Feature Syndicate, Inc.   9-14   JIM DAVIS

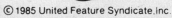

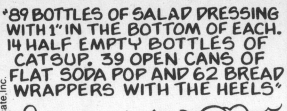

"I HATE MONDAY"

As you can see, Garfield's pet hate is MONDAY and the alarming regularity with which it arrives and although Garfield is renowned for his appetite, he's no "Glutton for Punishment".

WELL, I WONDER WHAT'S GOING TO HAPPEN TO ME TODAY

JIM DAVIS   12-27

BLAT!

© 1982 United Feature Syndicate, Inc.

MONDAY MOVES IN A MYSTERIOUS WAY

JIM DAVIS

JIM DAVIS

7-16

7-17

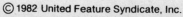

© 1982 United Feature Syndicate, Inc.

© 1982 United Feature Syndicate, Inc.

SWIPE!

I HATE MONDAYS

© 1981 United Feature Syndicate, Inc.

JIM DAVIS   9-7

HEE HEE

JIM DAVIS   9-8

HA HA HA!

WHEN YOU'RE BUILT LOW TO THE GROUND, A WALK IN THE GRASS CAN BE TICKLISH

© 1981 United Feature Syndicate, Inc.

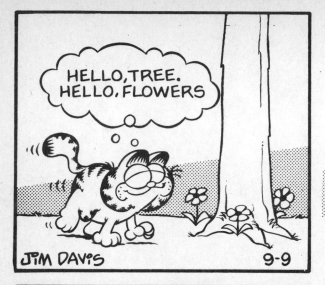

HELLO. I'M NERMAL, THE WORLD'S CUTEST KITTEN, HERE TO DO CUTE KITTEN THINGS IN ORDER TO CHARM THE PANTS OFF YOUR OWNER AND POINT OUT HOW UNCUTE YOU ARE

I HATE MONDAY

JIM DAVIS   6-21

© 1982 United Feature Syndicate, Inc.

GIMME THAT

I FAIL TO SEE WHAT'S SO CUTE ABOUT YARN

OR KITTENS, FOR THAT MATTER

JIM DAVIS   6-22

© 1982 United Feature Syndicate, Inc.

WHAT TIME IS IT, GARFIELD?

JIM DAVIS 2-24

© 1982 United Feature Syndicate, Inc.

WHAT AM I DOING? I CAN'T TELL TIME

JIM DAVIS

OKAY, GARFIELD. ONE BITE

© 1982 United Feature Syndicate, Inc. 2-26

JIM DAVIS

2-1

KABOOM

© 1982 United Feature Syndicate, Inc.

I HATE MONDAY

2-2

JIM DAVIS

© 1982 United Feature Syndicate, Inc.

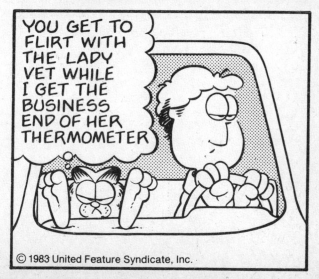

5-6

© 1981 United Feature Syndicate, Inc.

HOW DO YOU FEEL ABOUT JOGGING THIS MORNING, GARFIELD?

JIM DAVIS

5-7

HOW DO YOU FEEL ABOUT BLEEDING THIS MORNING

I GET YOUR DRIFT

BRIGHT LAD

© 1981 United Feature Syndicate, Inc.

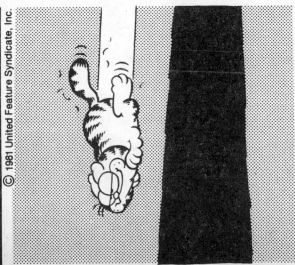

NICE TRY, GARFIELD, BUT I DON'T BUY YOUR STUPID WATERMELON DISGUISE

JIM DAVIS 3-23

© 1983 United Feature Syndicate, Inc.

RATA TATTA TATTA TATA

JIM DAVIS 3-24

DON'T MAKE FUN OF ODIE, GARFIELD. THAT'S NOT NICE

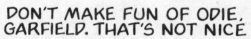

© 1983 United Feature Syndicate, Inc.

THAT'S EVEN LESS NICE

WELL, I WONDER WHAT'S GOING TO HAPPEN TO ME TODAY

JiM DAViS 12-27

BLAT!

© 1982 United Feature Syndicate, Inc.

MONDAY MOVES IN A MYSTERIOUS WAY

GO FETCH THE PAPER, GARFIELD

12-28 JiM DAViS

LOOK CLOSELY, JON. THESE ARE CAT'S PAWS, NOT SLAVE'S PAWS

© 1982 United Feature Syndicate, Inc.

I'LL IGNORE YOUR SMALL INDISCRETION THIS TIME, AND SPARE YOUR LIFE

THANK YOU, ...SIR

NIBBLE
NIBBLE
NIBBLE

IT'S NOT GOOD TO CHEW YOUR NAILS, GARFIELD

OH, THAT'S OKAY

I'M CHEWING ON ODIE'S

© 1982 United Feature Syndicate, Inc.

Z

I'M BORED. I NEED TO ADD SOME SPARKLE TO MY LIFE

Z

© 1982 United Feature Syndicate, Inc.

12-29 JIM DAVIS

JIM DAVIS 12-30

Garfield

Weighs in!

BY: JIM DAVIS

Weighs in!

Garfield loves to throw his weight around and he certainly has enough artillery to do so.

Enjoy a feast of gags as you watch Garfield heavy the scales of injustice in typical light hearted fashion!

GOBBLE!
GOBBLE!
GOBBLE!

© 1980 United Feature Syndicate, Inc.

THANKS FOR LEAVING A WING, GARFIELD

WHAT ARE FRIENDS FOR?

YOU LOOK GUILTY ABOUT SOMETHING, GARFIELD

DID YOU EAT MY PIE?

YOUR PEPPER STEAK

© 1980 United Feature Syndicate, Inc.

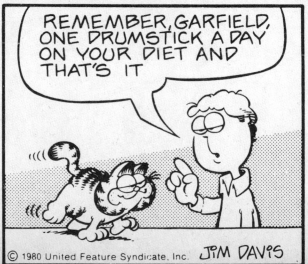

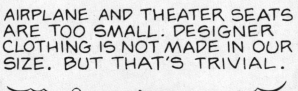

THE JUNGLE CAT AWAKES WITH A VORACIOUS APPETITE

© 1980 United Feature Syndicate, Inc.

6-9

HE INSTINCTIVELY SETS OUT TO SLAY SOME BREAKFAST

THAT WASN'T VERY PRETTY, BUT IT'S ALL PART OF THE FOOD CHAIN

JIM DAVIS

THE ALLEY CAT SCROUNGES FOR FOOD

6-10

HE POKES HIS HEAD INTO A PROMISING GARBAGE CAN

PEEEYEWWW!

© 1980 United Feature Syndicate, Inc.

JIM DAVIS

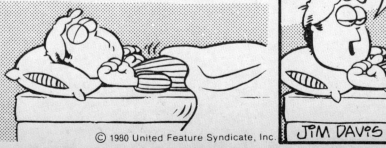

BASH!

7-16

GOOD MORNING, FATSO

ALL I DID WAS JUMP OFF THE BED

IT ISN'T HEALTHY FOR A CAT TO BE AS BIG AS YOU ARE, GARFIELD

JiM DAViS 7-17

WHY, YOU COULD GET HEART DISEASE, GET FALLEN ARCHES...

GET HARPOONED

COULDN'T RESIST IT COULD YOU

© 1981 United Feature Syndicate, Inc.

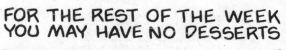

5-24

BLUT
BLUT
BLUT
BLUT
BLUT

© 1982 United Feature Syndicate, Inc.

WHEN ARE YOU GOING TO LEARN TO CONTROL THAT TEMPER OF YOURS, GARFIELD?

THE EXACT SAME INSTANT THEY INVENT AN EASY POURING CATSUP

I'LL CUT THE LASAGNA IN TWO PIECES, AND YOU TAKE FIRST PICK

JIM DAVIS

5-21

IT'S GETTING COLD, GARFIELD

© 1982 United Feature Syndicate, Inc.

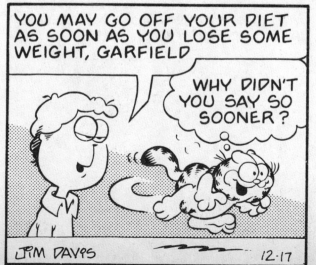

6-2

© 1982 United Feature Syndicate, Inc.

© 1982 United Feature Syndicate, Inc.

IT'S TIME YOU GO ON ANOTHER DIET, GARFIELD

6-28

1-7-84

© 1983 United Feature Syndicate, Inc.

© 1983 United Feature Syndicate, Inc.

© 1983 United Feature Syndicate, Inc.

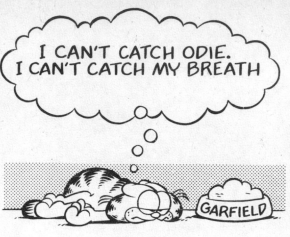

I'M TAKING THIS STEAK AND THERE'S NOTHING YOU CAN DO ABOUT IT, CHIPMUNK CHEEKS

© 1983 United Feature Syndicate, Inc.

I'VE ALWAYS ENCOURAGED GARFIELD TO BE ASSERTIVE. BUT I BELIEVE HE'S CROSSED THE FINE LINE TO OBNOXIOUS

CLANG!

HEY, GARFIELD, HOW DO YOU LIKE MY NEW DINNER BELL?

IT GOT MY ATTENTION

© 1983 United Feature Syndicate, Inc.

1-4-84

OH, NO! IT'S THE OLD "DISGUISE THE TONGUE AS A LOAF OF FRENCH BREAD" TRICK!

OKAY, WHO LOOSENED THE TOP ON MY SALTSHAKER?!

GARFIELD, THAT WASN'T VERY NICE

YOU'RE RIGHT. THAT WASN'T VERY NICE

BUT IT WAS EXTREMELY FUNNY

1-5-84

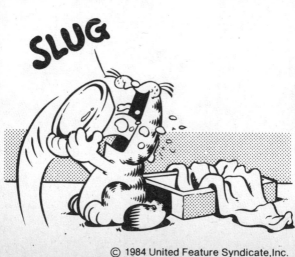